"THE SMALLEST FELINE IS A MASTERPIECE."

Leonardo da Vinci

ISBN: 978-0-578-69640-9

DEDICATION

To my One and Only...
the only One worthy of
99 beautiful names.

TESTIMONIALS

"This journal is an essential addition to any cat lover's bookshelf! It is a great resource for anyone who owns a cat. When filled out properly, it gives the owner a great peace of mind... highly recommended!"

DR. CORINNE FISHER, VETERINARIAN
Crossroads Animal Hospital

"What About the Cat? is a must have for cats and their owners! If you love your cat you need to get this book for them! I will be recommending to all my friends."

CHRIS UNANGST
Approved All Breed Judge, The International Cat Association (TICA)

"In my opinion What About the Cat? has everything anyone could possibly think of... it's absolutely essential... Christine has thought of everything."

CATHY HARTLEY
Owner, Kitty City Salon
C.F.M. Certified Feline Master Groomer
C.M.C.G. Certified Master Cat Groomer

DISCLAIMER

This book is not intended as a substitute for the medical advice of veterinarians or the behavioral advice of animal professionals. The reader should always consult a trained, licensed and certified professional in matters relating to their cat's physical and/or mental health and particularly with respect to any symptoms that may require diagnosis or medical attention.

WHAT ABOUT the CAT ?

Everything You Need to Know About My Cat's Care (In Case I'm Not Around to Ask!)

Christine Ciana Calabrese

Table of Contents

ACKNOWLEDGMENTS

Special thanks to the following individuals who encouraged the publication and promotion of this book:

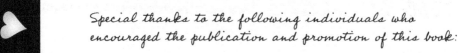

- Stacey Edge of MOMENTUM Creative Integration for her continued support and all of her design prowess.

- Jen McFarland of Women Conquer Business for her business coaching and reminding me to pat myself on the back once in awhile.

- Cheryl Hague for her endless patience with me in discussing all things cat related.

- And Tricia Militello and Crystal Broccardo for believing in every outlandish manifestation I concocted.

"Cats are mercurial creatures, making their transition into new homes especially challenging. Cats only tell us what they want us to know. In this important book, Ms. Calabrese provides new caregivers with more than a data list; *What About the Cat?* is a 'Book of Secrets', that delves into the mind of the cat. With everything from important medical history to a list of favorite toys, foods, grooming, and quirky behaviors, this essential journal becomes a unique resource for new caregivers. The book reveals the wants, needs, and desires of your cat. Rest assured, should you not be around to continue caring for your beloved cat, this guide will ensure a smooth transition into your cat's next life."

CHERYL HAGUE
TICA/CFA Exotic Shorthair Breeder/Exhibitor,
Former TICA Exotic Shorthair Breed Council Chair

"I've come to the conclusion after much consideration, research and consultation...

Cats: They're not dogs.

Nonetheless, these bewitching, complex, independent creatures require preplanning just as much as their canine counterparts, if not more! The creation of this journal was my way of doing my best to ensure that cat owners' beloved cats would be cared for in the most thoughtful way possible, by someone else, should those cat owners become unable to care for their cats anymore, for whatever reason. The Helpful Tips in between sections are a combination of expert advice and the culmination of personal experience as a professional pet sitter; they are only suggestions and by no means should ever replace the recommendations of your veterinarian or behaviorist. I also highly encourage consulting an estate planning attorney to discuss the best way to financially preplan for your cat's extended care."

Warmly,
Christine Ciana Calabrese

"I have been rescuing dogs and cats for over forty years and many of the cats I have rescued have been seniors that had lived good lives, in comfy homes, and then because of a lack of preplanning, inevitably ended up in a shelter. Others cats I've encountered have had inadequate life plans that unfortunately resulted in severe consequences for those cats, as well. My passion with Famous Fido Rescue is to help prevent animals from entering and/or re-entering shelters. What About the Cat? is a purr-fect way for a cat's guardian to plan for their cat's well-being by developing a solid, thoughtful life plan for their cat while keeping all of their pertinent information in one convenient place."

GLORIA LISSNER

Founder of Famous Fido Rescue Wellness
& Learning Center

7 WAYS TO GET THE MOST OUT OF THIS BOOK

1. This book is designed to accommodate information for four cats that are being rehomed to the same household. If you have more than four cats, or know that the cats will be rehomed separately, please consider acquiring additional copies of this book, this way all caregivers are ensured to have the proper information.

2. Fill this book out as soon as possible.

3. Choose your cat's caregiver wisely and have a discussion with that person as to your specific wishes.

4. Tell your cat's caregiver about this book and where you will keep it. Consider keeping this book in plain view so that it can be easily referenced in case of an emergency. You may also want to discuss additional important paperwork (e.g., wills, trusts, insurance, etc.) as it pertains to your cat's care and financial support.

5. Have a successor caregiver listed for your cat in the event that circumstances change.

6. Review and update the information in this book as changes occur; this is especially important as your cat ages and/or develops potential medical or behavioral conditions.

7. IMPORTANT: MAKE SURE YOUR CAT'S MICROCHIP AND ID TAG INFORMATION IS UP TO DATE, IF APPLICABLE.

6 WAYS TO INTRODUCE A CAT TO A NEW HOME

Introducing any cat to a new home is stressful, but there are a few steps you can take to make for a more comfortable transition.

1. Don't introduce a cat to the entire house all at once: choose a room for the first few days to let the cat get acclimated to all the new smells and sounds of the new home with the door closed. Baby gates are very helpful for creating safe boundaries within the home, as an additional buffer, when other animals or small children are in the residence. Prior to a physical meeting, the new cat and other animals in the residence should be allowed to "meet" by sniffing each other under the door. Make sure that aside from providing food and water, the room is also equipped with a litter box, scratching post and toys.

2. Study the cat's history, if known, and determine whether the cat has an aversion to children or other animals. If so, modifications will need to be made since it is unreasonable to assume that the cat will acclimate to these aversions. Even if the cat does not have a known aversion to children or other animals, it is advisable to initially limit all interactions between the cat and children or other animals. These introductions should occur gradually and on a limited basis to ensure the children's and the cat's safety and comfort.

3. Create a "safe space" that is not accessible to children or other animals that the cat can retreat to if he or she feels frightened or needs space. This space can be a travel carrier LEFT OPEN with comfortable bedding inside, placed in a quiet part of the house that the cat can readily access. A cat tree is also a good safe space alternative. Stressed cats are prone to shed more.

4. If the cat's medical history is unknown or the cat has not been seen by a veterinarian in at least a year, the new cat should be seen by a veterinarian immediately to get a clean bill of health. Cats are masters of hiding ailments and illnesses so assumptions should never be made. **IMPORTANT:** take note of if your cat is eating and drinking, and how much during the first few days. Stressed cats do not eat or drink and can possibly develop a condition known as Fatty Liver (Hepatic Lipidosis), which can be fatal if untreated.

5. With any new pet, establish a routine as soon as possible. Animals appreciate patterns and consistency just as humans do. Consistency in feeding times, water bowl placement, litterbox, scratching post and cat tree location will help your new cat become comfortable more quickly.

6. Be patient and be calm. In time, the cat will adapt, but animals are very perceptive and are affected by others' energy and emotional states, so it is very important to be as calm as possible during this transition. If the cat seems to be having difficulty settling in, consult your veterinarian and/or a reputable animal behaviorist.

6 WAYS TO INTRODUCE A CAT TO A NEW HOME

Date this book was filled out and/or revised:

MY CAT(S)

and

Add photos here!

Date this book was filled out and/or revised:

MY CAT(S)

and

Add photos here!

In case of emergency, please answer the following questions for the immediate care of my cats.

Name of cat being rehomed:

OWNER

Name:

Address:

Phone:

E-mail:

CO-OWNER *(If applicable)*

Name:

Address:

Phone:

E-mail:

Notes:

Notes:

Designated Caregiver(s) for My Cat(s)

This is the person who is authorized to take my cat(s) and this book in case of emergency.

Name of cat(s) being rehomed:

Caregiver's name:

Address:

Phone:

E-mail:

Successor Caregiver(s) for My Cat(s)

This is the person who is authorized to take my cat(s) and this book should the caregiver(s) listed above be unwilling or unable to care for my cat(s).

Name of cat(s) being rehomed:

Caregiver's name:

Address:

Phone:

E-mail:

Notes:

Name of cat being rehomed:	
Nickname of cat:	
My cat is on medication:	❑ YES ❑ NO

If YES, name and location of medication:

My cat's food is located:

My cat normally wears a collar inside the house.	❑ YES ❑ NO

If NO, the collar can be found in this location in my home:

If my situation or hospitalization is only temporary, I would prefer that my cat stays in my home:	❑ YES ❑ NO

If my cat must leave my home, please be sure to take the following items with him/her (e.g., bed, toys, food, bowls, etc.):

The items accompanying my cat can be found in these locations in my home:

The location of my cat's carrier and towels can be found in these locations in my home:

Name of cat being rehomed:
Nickname of cat:
My cat is on medication: ❑ YES   ❑ NO
If YES, name and location of medication:
My cat's food is located:
My cat normally wears a collar inside the house.   ❑ YES   ❑ NO
If NO, the collar can be found in this location in my home:
If my situation or hospitalization is only temporary, I would prefer that my cat stays in my home: ❑ YES   ❑ NO
If my cat must leave my home, please be sure to take the following items with him/her (e.g., bed, toys, food, bowls, etc.):
The items accompanying my cat can be found in these locations in my home:
The location of my cat's carrier and towels can be found in these locations in my home:

Name of cat being rehomed:

Nickname of cat:

My cat is on medication: ❏ YES ❏ NO

If YES, name and location of medication:

My cat's food is located:

My cat normally wears a collar inside the house. ❏ YES ❏ NO

If NO, the collar can be found in this location in my home:

If my situation or hospitalization is only temporary, I would prefer that my cat stays in my home: ❏ YES ❏ NO

If my cat must leave my home, please be sure to take the following items with him/her (e.g., bed, toys, food, bowls, etc.):

The items accompanying my cat can be found in these locations in my home:

The location of my cat's carrier and towels can be found in these locations in my home:

Name of cat being rehomed:
Nickname of cat:
My cat is on medication: ❏ YES   ❏ NO
If YES, name and location of medication:
My cat's food is located:
My cat normally wears a collar inside the house.   ❏ YES   ❏ NO
If NO, the collar can be found in this location in my home:
If my situation or hospitalization is only temporary, I would prefer that my cat stays in my home: ❏ YES   ❏ NO
If my cat must leave my home, please be sure to take the following items with him/her (e.g., bed, toys, food, bowls, etc.):
The items accompanying my cat can be found in these locations in my home:
The location of my cat's carrier and towels can be found in these locations in my home:

Name of cat being rehomed:

Breed:

Sex: Birthday:

Color: Weight:

Animal hospital name:

Veterinarian name:

Address:

Phone:

Hours:

Name and contact information where cat originally came from (breeder, pet store, etc.):

Overview of medical conditions and/or diagnoses:

List medications and dosages:

My cat is an indoor/outdoor cat:		❑ YES	❑ NO

My cat is declawed:		❑ YES	❑ NO
Circle one: Front	Rear	All	

My cat has bred: ❑ YES ❑ NO

Date of last rabies vaccination:

Date of other vaccinations: *(If applicable)*
Feline panleukopenia virus:

Feline herpesvirus-1:

Calicivirus: Other:

Date of last Feline Leukemia/FIV test:

I treat my cat for fleas and ticks: *(Circle one)*
    Monthly   Seasonally
    As Needed   Not at All

Flea and tick prevention brand:

Date of last dental cleaning:

My cat is spayed/neutered: ❑ YES ❑ NO

My cat is microchipped: ❑ YES ❑ NO

Microchip company:

Microchip ID number:

Microchip Phone:

Registered person:

Address:

Phone:

Name of cat being rehomed:

Breed:

Sex: Birthday:

Color: Weight:

Animal hospital name:

Veterinarian name:

Address:

Phone:

Hours:

Name and contact information where cat originally came from (breeder, pet store, etc.):

Overview of medical conditions and/or diagnoses:

List medications and dosages:

My cat is an indoor/outdoor cat:	❑ YES	❑ NO
My cat is declawed:	❑ YES	❑ NO
Circle one: Front Rear All		
My cat has bred:	❑ YES	❑ NO

Date of last rabies vaccination:

Date of other vaccinations: *(If applicable)*
Feline panleukopenia virus:

Feline herpesvirus-1:

Calicivirus: Other:

Date of last Feline Leukemia/FIV test:

I treat my cat for fleas and ticks: *(Circle one)*
    Monthly   Seasonally
    As Needed   Not at All

Flea and tick prevention brand:

Date of last dental cleaning:

My cat is spayed/neutered:	❑ YES	❑ NO
My cat is microchipped:	❑ YES	❑ NO

Microchip company:

Microchip ID number:

Microchip Phone:

Registered person:

Address:

Phone:

VETERINARY INFORMATION

23

Name of cat being rehomed:

Breed:

Sex: Birthday:

Color: Weight:

Animal hospital name:

Veterinarian name:

Address:

Phone:

Hours:

Name and contact information where cat originally came from (breeder, pet store, etc.):

Overview of medical conditions and/or diagnoses:

List medications and dosages:

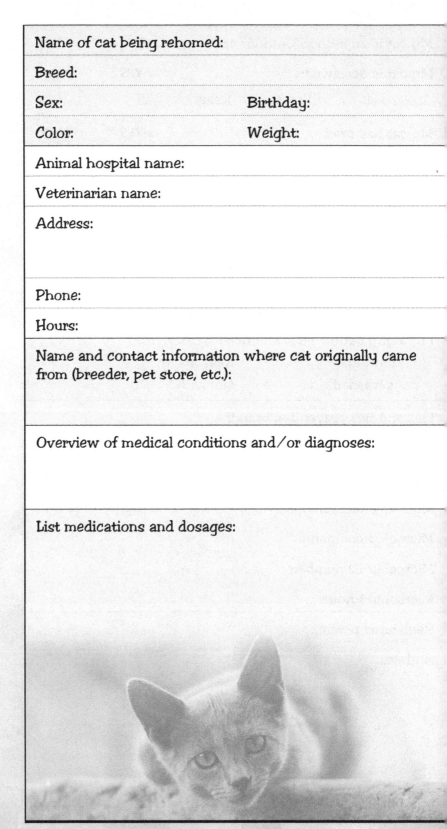

My cat is an indoor/outdoor cat:		❏ YES	❏ NO

My cat is declawed:		❏ YES	❏ NO
Circle one:	Front	Rear	All

My cat has bred:		❏ YES	❏ NO

Date of last rabies vaccination:

Date of other vaccinations: *(If applicable)*
Feline panleukopenia virus:

Feline herpesvirus-1:

Calicivirus: Other:

Date of last Feline Leukemia/FIV test:

I treat my cat for fleas and ticks: *(Circle one)*
    Monthly   Seasonally
    As Needed   Not at All

Flea and tick prevention brand:

Date of last dental cleaning:

My cat is spayed/neutered:		❏ YES	❏ NO

My cat is microchipped:		❏ YES	❏ NO

Microchip company:

Microchip ID number:

Microchip Phone:

Registered person:

Address:

Phone:

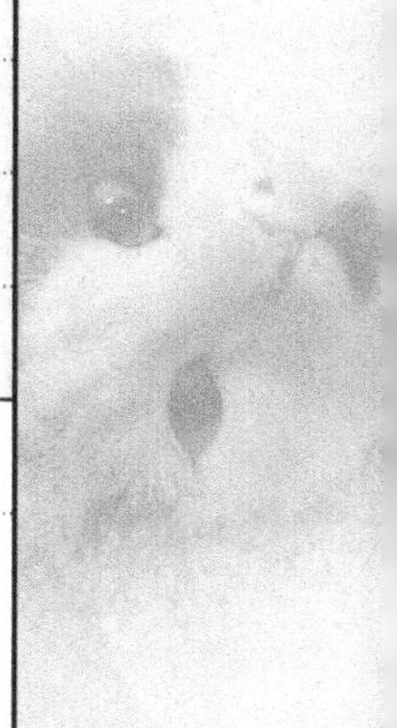

Name of cat being rehomed:

Breed:

Sex: Birthday:

Color: Weight:

Animal hospital name:

Veterinarian name:

Address:

Phone:

Hours:

Name and contact information where cat originally came from (breeder, pet store, etc.):

Overview of medical conditions and/or diagnoses:

List medications and dosages:

My cat is an indoor/outdoor cat:	❏ YES	❏ NO

My cat is declawed:	❏ YES	❏ NO
Circle one: Front Rear All		

My cat has bred:	❏ YES	❏ NO

Date of last rabies vaccination:

Date of other vaccinations: *(If applicable)*
Feline panleukopenia virus:

Feline herpesvirus-1:

Calicivirus: Other:

Date of last Feline Leukemia/FIV test:

I treat my cat for fleas and ticks: *(Circle one)*
   Monthly   Seasonally
   As Needed   Not at All

Flea and tick prevention brand:

Date of last dental cleaning:

My cat is spayed/neutered:	❏ YES	❏ NO

My cat is microchipped:	❏ YES	❏ NO

Microchip company:

Microchip ID number:

Microchip Phone:

Registered person:

Address:

Phone:

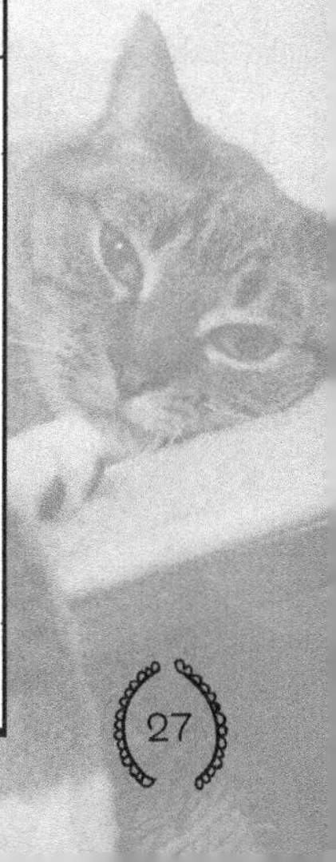

Helpful Tips!

🐾 The preceding information can be obtained in more detail from the cat's veterinarian. If the caregiver will be using a different veterinarian due to proximity from the caregiver's home, the caregiver will need to request the cat's current veterinarian copy and send the cat's medical records to the new veterinarian.

🐾 If you are one of those pet parents who are concerned about potentially over-vaccinating your cat, speak to your veterinarian about having a titers test; a titer is a measurement of a specific antibody in the blood. This blood test will indicate if your cat still has adequate immunity to a certain disease from a previous vaccination.

🐾 Do not forget to tell your cat's caregiver to update the microchip information when they take on caring for your cat. Call the microchip company listed in this book and update changes of address and phone numbers. If microchip information is not provided in this book, a veterinarian or animal shelter should be able to scan the cat and tell you which company has registered the microchip.

🐾 If you live alone with your cat, consider having a keychain and/or a wallet notecard made stating that your cat is home alone, in case of emergency; also have a phone number available for a first responder to contact.

🐾 Additionally, you can purchase static cling window decals for your home so that in case of a fire, first responders are aware that your cat is inside.

Notes:

Name of cat being rehomed:

| My cat has special needs? | ❏ YES | ❏ NO |

If YES, my cat is: (Circle all)

Blind	Deaf	Diabetic
Epileptic	Paralyzed	Arthritic
Other:		

My cat: (Circle all)

| uses a ramp | uses stairs | is picked up/down |
| Other: | | |

| My cat wears a diaper: | ❏ YES | ❏ NO |

If YES, how often is diaper changed?

| My cat is prone to urinary issues: | ❏ YES | ❏ NO |

| My cat is prone to rashes or other skin conditions: | ❏ YES | ❏ NO |

| My cat uses a wheelchair: | ❏ YES | ❏ NO |

If YES, how long is the cat in the wheelchair at any given time?

Company and contact information for where the wheelchair can be taken or sent for repairs:

| Does the wheelchair have a warranty? | ❏ YES | ❏ NO |

| My cat has a different set of special needs than those listed above: | ❏ YES | ❏ NO |

If YES, please explain:

Name of cat being rehomed:		
My cat has special needs?	❏ YES	❏ NO

If YES, my cat is: *(Circle all)*

Blind	Deaf	Diabetic
Epileptic	Paralyzed	Arthritic
Other:		

My cat: *(Circle all)*

uses a ramp	uses stairs	is picked up/down
Other:		

My cat wears a diaper:	❏ YES	❏ NO
If YES, how often is diaper changed?		
My cat is prone to urinary issues:	❏ YES	❏ NO
My cat is prone to rashes or other skin conditions:	❏ YES	❏ NO
My cat uses a wheelchair:	❏ YES	❏ NO

If YES, how long is the cat in the wheelchair at any given time?

Company and contact information for where the wheelchair can be taken or sent for repairs:

Does the wheelchair have a warranty?	❏ YES	❏ NO
My cat has a different set of special needs than those listed above:	❏ YES	❏ NO

If YES, please explain:

Name of cat being rehomed:		

My cat has special needs?	❏ YES	❏ NO

If YES, my cat is: *(Circle all)*

Blind	Deaf	Diabetic
Epileptic	Paralyzed	Arthritic
Other:		

My cat: *(Circle all)*

uses a ramp	uses stairs	is picked up/down
Other:		

My cat wears a diaper:	❏ YES	❏ NO

If YES, how often is diaper changed?

My cat is prone to urinary issues:	❏ YES	❏ NO

My cat is prone to rashes or other skin conditions:	❏ YES	❏ NO

My cat uses a wheelchair:	❏ YES	❏ NO

If YES, how long is the cat in the wheelchair at any given time?

Company and contact information for where the wheelchair can be taken or sent for repairs:

Does the wheelchair have a warranty?	❏ YES	❏ NO

My cat has a different set of special needs than those listed above:	❏ YES	❏ NO

If YES, please explain:

Name of cat being rehomed:		
My cat has special needs?	❑ YES	❑ NO

If YES, my cat is: *(Circle all)*

Blind	Deaf	Diabetic
Epileptic	Paralyzed	Arthritic
Other:		

My cat: *(Circle all)*

uses a ramp	uses stairs	is picked up/down
Other:		

My cat wears a diaper:	❑ YES	❑ NO

If YES, how often is diaper changed?

My cat is prone to urinary issues:	❑ YES	❑ NO
My cat is prone to rashes or other skin conditions:	❑ YES	❑ NO
My cat uses a wheelchair:	❑ YES	❑ NO

If YES, how long is the cat in the wheelchair at any given time?

Company and contact information for where the wheelchair can be taken or sent for repairs:

Does the wheelchair have a warranty?	❑ YES	❑ NO
My cat has a different set of special needs than those listed above:	❑ YES	❑ NO

If YES, please explain:

🐾 Cats that wear special equipment for mobility are no different from humans in that they also chafe and develop pressure sores. Be conscious of how long your cat wears his or her equipment and check areas where skin and equipment come into contact frequently.

🐾 Just because a cat can still physically **DO** something does not necessarily mean they **SHOULD**, particularly when it comes to jumping on and off furniture. If you have an older cat or a cat with physical challenges, consider getting him or her a small set of stairs or a cat ramp for furniture. This kind of equipment can be purchased at almost any pet supply store. The repeated impact of landing on front paws at steep angles may inevitably have a detrimental effect on shoulder joints, as well as other areas.

🐾 Use caution when approaching blind and/or deaf cats when sleeping as not to startle them. You can pat the floor near them or gently blow on them to rouse them before you attempt to touch them.

🐾 If your cat is struggling with arthritis, consider getting a litter box with a shallow tray; sometimes older arthritic cats stop using their litter boxes because of the discomfort it causes to step into a box that requires too big of a step for them.

🐾 Arthritic cats may also benefit from heated cat beds to ease discomfort; be sure to read product reviews thoroughly.

I have prepared an estate plan?   ❑ YES   ❑ NO

My estate planning documents are located:

The documents I have include:

The name and contact information of my attorney:

I have purchased life insurance: ❑ YES   ❑ NO

If YES, name of insurance company?

A copy of my life insurance policy is located:

NOTE: Your veterinarian will have copies of your cat's medical records, but if you
have additional documentation that you would like your caregiver to have, please
include the type and location of those documents. If you have pet insurance,
your veterinarian will also have those records, but it is important to provide
policy numbers, copies of policies, and contact information to your caregiver.

Notes:

Name of cat being rehomed:

My cat is ok being picked up: ❏ YES ❏ NO

♡ = areas my cat likes to be touched
X = areas my cat does NOT like to be touched

RIGHT SIDE   LEFT SIDE

My cat is fearful overall: ❏ YES ❏ NO

My cat has bitten out of fear in the past: ❏ YES ❏ NO

My cat has the following specific phobias:

My cat's favorite place to hide is:

My cat has medication for specific phobias: ❏ YES ❏ NO

If YES, please name medication and dosage:

My cat wears a Thundershirt™: ❏ YES ❏ NO

If YES, what size?

My cat wears an Anxiety Wrap™: ❏ YES ❏ NO

If YES, what size?

Name of cat being rehomed:		
My cat is ok being picked up:	❏ YES	❏ NO

= areas my cat likes to be touched
= areas my cat does NOT like to be touched

RIGHT SIDE   LEFT SIDE

My cat is fearful overall:	❏ YES	❏ NO
My cat has bitten out of fear in the past:	❏ YES	❏ NO
My cat has the following specific phobias:		
My cat's favorite place to hide is:		
My cat has medication for specific phobias:	❏ YES	❏ NO
If YES, please name medication and dosage:		
My cat wears a Thundershirt™:	❏ YES	❏ NO
If YES, what size?		
My cat wears an Anxiety Wrap™:	❏ YES	❏ NO
If YES, what size?		

Name of cat being rehomed:		
My cat is ok being picked up:	❏ YES	❏ NO

♡ = areas my cat likes to be touched
X = areas my cat does NOT like to be touched

RIGHT SIDE   LEFT SIDE

My cat is fearful overall:	❏ YES	❏ NO
My cat has bitten out of fear in the past:	❏ YES	❏ NO
My cat has the following specific phobias:		
My cat's favorite place to hide is:		
My cat has medication for specific phobias:	❏ YES	❏ NO
If YES, please name medication and dosage:		
My cat wears a Thundershirt™:	❏ YES	❏ NO
If YES, what size?		
My cat wears an Anxiety Wrap™:	❏ YES	❏ NO
If YES, what size?		

Name of cat being rehomed:

My cat is ok being picked up: ❏ YES ❏ NO

= areas my cat likes to be touched
= areas my cat does NOT like to be touched

RIGHT SIDE LEFT SIDE

My cat is fearful overall: ❏ YES ❏ NO

My cat has bitten out of fear in the past: ❏ YES ❏ NO

My cat has the following specific phobias:

My cat's favorite place to hide is:

My cat has medication for specific phobias: ❏ YES ❏ NO

If YES, please name medication and dosage:

My cat wears a Thundershirt™: ❏ YES ❏ NO

If YES, what size?

My cat wears an Anxiety Wrap™: ❏ YES ❏ NO

If YES, what size?

Helpful Tips!

- 🐾 Speak to your veterinarian about incorporating holistic aids such as Zylkene or Solliquin or any natural supplements to help calm your cat, especially during the transition period and other stressful situations.

- 🐾 Make sure your cat has an easily accessible "safe space" that he/she can retreat to if feeling scared or threatened.

- 🐾 There is a saying "Let sleeping dogs lie"; in a similar vein "Let hiding cats hide". Please resist the urge to extract your cat from their hiding place, simply for the sake of being seen. As long as their location is known and they are not ill or in danger, they should be allowed to come out when they are comfortable.

- 🐾 Calming music played for your cat is a good tool in helping reduce your cat's stress levels. Check online at: ww.musicforcats.com and www.Icalmpet.com

- 🐾 Feliway is a synthetic copy of the feline facial pheromone which is used by cats to mark their territory as safe and secure. By imitating a cat's natural facial pheromones, Feliway creates a state of familiarity and security in the cat's local environment. This in turn helps comfort and reassure cats while they cope with a challenging situation; it also aids in the prevention and/or reduces the stress caused by a change in their environment. Available in spray or diffuser.

Name of cat being rehomed:

My cat knows these words/commands:

My cat knows these tricks:

I reward above tricks with: (Circle all)
    Praise   Petting   Treats   A toy

My cat likes socializing with humans overall:
    ❑ YES   ❑ NO   ❑ SOMETIMES

My cat is most active at: (Circle all)
    Morning   Daytime   Dusk   Nightime

My cat likes to head-bump humans:
    ❑ YES   ❑ NO   ❑ SOMETIMES

My cat likes to lick people: ❑ YES ❑ NO ❑ SOMETIMES

My cat likes to "knead" humans with paws (generally before getting comfortable): ❑ YES ❑ NO ❑ SOMETIMES

My cat is a play-biter: ❑ YES ❑ NO ❑ SOMETIMES

My cat makes unusual noises periodically, such as: (Circle all)
    Chattering   Chirping   Howling
    Growling   Other:

These noises are associated with:

My cat chews on items: ❑ YES ❑ NO ❑ SOMETIMES

Some of these items may be:

My cat scratches on items: ❑ YES ❑ NO ❑ SOMETIMES

Some of these items may be:

Please list any quirky behaviors and/or unique traits:

Name of cat being rehomed:

My cat knows these words/commands:

My cat knows these tricks:

I reward above tricks with: (Circle all)
    Praise   Petting   Treats   A toy

My cat likes socializing with humans overall:
  ❏ YES   ❏ NO   ❏ SOMETIMES

My cat is most active at: (Circle all)
  Morning   Daytime   Dusk   Nightime

My cat likes to head-bump humans:
  ❏ YES   ❏ NO   ❏ SOMETIMES

My cat likes to lick people: ❏ YES ❏ NO ❏ SOMETIMES

My cat likes to "knead" humans with paws (generally before getting comfortable): ❏ YES ❏ NO ❏ SOMETIMES

My cat is a play-biter: ❏ YES ❏ NO ❏ SOMETIMES

My cat makes unusual noises periodically, such as: (Circle all)
  Chattering   Chirping   Howling
  Growling   Other:

These noises are associated with:

My cat chews on items: ❏ YES ❏ NO ❏ SOMETIMES

Some of these items may be:

My cat scratches on items: ❏ YES ❏ NO ❏ SOMETIMES

Some of these items may be:

Please list any quirky behaviors and/or unique traits:

Name of cat being rehomed:

My cat knows these words/commands:

My cat knows these tricks:

I reward above tricks with: *(Circle all)*

Praise   Petting   Treats   A toy

My cat likes socializing with humans overall:

❏ YES   ❏ NO   ❏ SOMETIMES

My cat is most active at: *(Circle all)*

Morning   Daytime   Dusk   Nightime

My cat likes to head-bump humans:

❏ YES   ❏ NO   ❏ SOMETIMES

My cat likes to lick people: ❏ YES   ❏ NO   ❏ SOMETIMES

My cat likes to "knead" humans with paws (generally before getting comfortable):   ❏ YES   ❏ NO   ❏ SOMETIMES

My cat is a play-biter: ❏ YES   ❏ NO   ❏ SOMETIMES

My cat makes unusual noises periodically, such as: *(Circle all)*

Chattering   Chirping   Howling
Growling   Other:

These noises are associated with:

My cat chews on items: ❏ YES   ❏ NO   ❏ SOMETIMES

Some of these items may be:

My cat scratches on items: ❏ YES   ❏ NO   ❏ SOMETIMES

Some of these items may be:

Please list any quirky behaviors and/or unique traits:

Name of cat being rehomed:

My cat knows these words/commands:

My cat knows these tricks:

I reward above tricks with: *(Circle all)*

Praise   Petting   Treats   A toy

My cat likes socializing with humans overall:

❑ YES   ❑ NO   ❑ SOMETIMES

My cat is most active at: *(Circle all)*

Morning   Daytime   Dusk   Nightime

My cat likes to head-bump humans:

❑ YES   ❑ NO   ❑ SOMETIMES

My cat likes to lick people: ❑ YES   ❑ NO   ❑ SOMETIMES

My cat likes to "knead" humans with paws (generally before getting comfortable):   ❑ YES   ❑ NO   ❑ SOMETIMES

My cat is a play-biter: ❑ YES   ❑ NO   ❑ SOMETIMES

My cat makes unusual noises periodically, such as: *(Circle all)*

Chattering   Chirping   Howling
Growling   Other:

These noises are associated with:

My cat chews on items: ❑ YES   ❑ NO   ❑ SOMETIMES

Some of these items may be:

My cat scratches on items: ❑ YES   ❑ NO   ❑ SOMETIMES

Some of these items may be:

Please list any quirky behaviors and/or unique traits:

🐾 Please be aware that cats can have a tendency to circle their human's legs while the human is walking: this can be a potential tripping hazard if there are elderly humans in the house so always remain vigilant to avoid falls.

🐾 Please watch cats for hazardous chewing behavior. Power cords and certain plant chewing can result in illness, injury or death. The ASPCA has compiled the following list of plants that are toxic to cats:

➡ www.aspca.org/pet-care/animal-poison-control/toxic-and-non-toxic-plants

🐾 Furniture scratching can be preventing by supplying your cat with a couple of scratching posts (preferably on each level of your home.) Deterring your cat from scratching furniture can be done by temporarily covering the furniture area with tin foil or double-sided tape. Introduce your cat to the new scratching post which should be taller than they are and very sturdy and stable. Consider a pheromone spray on the post, such as Feliway, to make it more attractive to your cat. To encourage initial use, hold a toy or treat above your cat, in front of the new post. Reward the cat when they touch the post, to create positive association.

🐾 Scratching posts come in different materials and textures (such as carpeted or cardboard.) Be open to trying a few different types to see which your cat is most attracted to.

🐾 It's a good idea to leave your carrier out in plain view, preferably with the door open, so that the cat does not develop a negative/fearful association with it only being for veterinary visits.

Notes:

Name of cat being rehomed:

My cat eats this brand of food:
❑ WET:
❑ DRY:
❑ RAW FRESH:
❑ RAW FROZEN:

It can be purchased at:

The quantity of food at each meal is:

Add this additive(s) to each meal:

It can be purchased at:

My cat's food is left out all day:　　❑ YES　　❑ NO

If NO, what are the feeding times?

My cat uses a slow feeder cat bowl or a food puzzle:
　❑ YES　　❑ NO　　SPECIFY:

My cat uses a self-feeder or timed feeder:
　❑ YES　　❑ NO　　SPECIFY:

My cat drinks out of a water fountain bowl:　　❑ YES　　❑ NO

If YES, how often is it cleaned?

Is there a filter, if so, how often is it replaced?　　❑ YES　　❑ NO

My cat's favorite treats are:

List any special feeding instructions:

Notes:

Name of cat being rehomed:

My cat eats this brand of food:
- ❑ WET:
- ❑ DRY:
- ❑ RAW FRESH:
- ❑ RAW FROZEN:

It can be purchased at:

The quantity of food at each meal is:

Add this additive(s) to each meal:

It can be purchased at:

My cat´s food is left out all day: ❑ YES   ❑ NO

If NO, what are the feeding times?

My cat uses a slow feeder cat bowl or a food puzzle:

❑ YES   ❑ NO   SPECIFY:

My cat uses a self-feeder or timed feeder:

❑ YES   ❑ NO   SPECIFY:

My cat drinks out of a water fountain bowl: ❑ YES   ❑ NO

If YES, how often is it cleaned?

Is there a filter, if so, how often is it replaced?   ❑ YES   ❑ NO

My cat's favorite treats are:

List any special feeding instructions:

Notes:

Name of cat being rehomed:

My cat eats this brand of food:
- ❏ WET:
- ❏ DRY:
- ❏ RAW FRESH:
- ❏ RAW FROZEN:

It can be purchased at:

The quantity of food at each meal is:

Add this additive(s) to each meal:

It can be purchased at:

My cat's food is left out all day:　　　❏ YES　　❏ NO

If NO, what are the feeding times?

My cat uses a slow feeder cat bowl or a food puzzle:

　　❏ YES　　❏ NO　　SPECIFY:

My cat uses a self-feeder or timed feeder:

　　❏ YES　　❏ NO　　SPECIFY:

My cat drinks out of a water fountain bowl:　　❏ YES　　❏ NO

If YES, how often is it cleaned?

Is there a filter, if so, how often is it replaced?　　❏ YES　　❏ NO

My cat's favorite treats are:

List any special feeding instructions:

Notes:

Name of cat being rehomed:

My cat eats this brand of food:
❑ WET:
❑ DRY:
❑ RAW FRESH:
❑ RAW FROZEN:

It can be purchased at:

The quantity of food at each meal is:

Add this additive(s) to each meal:

It can be purchased at:

My cat´s food is left out all day:　　　　❑ YES　　　❑ NO

If NO, what are the feeding times?

My cat uses a slow feeder cat bowl or a food puzzle:
　　❑ YES　　　❑ NO　　　SPECIFY:

My cat uses a self-feeder or timed feeder:
　　❑ YES　　　❑ NO　　　SPECIFY:

My cat drinks out of a water fountain bowl:　　❑ YES　　　❑ NO

If YES, how often is it cleaned?

Is there a filter, if so, how often is it replaced?　　❑ YES　　　❑ NO

My cat's favorite treats are:

List any special feeding instructions:

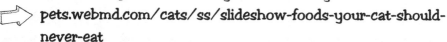

Helpful Tips!

🐾 *Fetch* by *WebMD* has come out with a list of foods that are toxic to your cat, which include, but are not limited to: onions, garlic, chives, grapes, raisins and liver. For a complete list of foods, please consult your veterinarian. You can also reference the *Fetch* by *WebMD* through the following link:

▷ pets.webmd.com/cats/ss/slideshow-foods-your-cat-should-never-eat

🐾 Unlike cats which are omnivores, cats are true carnivores and need meat in their diet. NEVER feed a cat a vegetarian diet. An excellent resource to consult when selecting your cat's diet is the book *Dr. Pitcairn's Complete Guide to Natural Health for Dogs and Cats*. It provides a wonderful introductory explanation of cat's nutritional requirements and also offers recipes that owners can make themselves, if so inclined. Consult your own veterinarian with additional questions or concerns.

🐾 Food and water bowls should be washed daily; bacteria can accumulate in the bowl and potentially harm your cat's health. Stainless steel bowls and porcelain bowls are recommended instead of plastic bowls.

Name of cat being rehomed:

Time of day my cat is the most active: *(Circle all)*

Morning   Daytime   Dusk   Nighttime

My cat's playtime with me is usually:

My cat's favorite toys are:

My cat's favorite game to play with a human is:

I take my cats for outdoor walks:	❑ YES	❑ NO
If YES, my cat walks on a harness:	❑ YES	❑ NO
My cat rides in a stroller:	❑ YES	❑ NO

Name of cat being rehomed:

Time of day my cat is the most active: *(Circle all)*

Morning   Daytime   Dusk   Nighttime

My cat's playtime with me is usually:

My cat's favorite toys are:

My cat's favorite game to play with a human is:

I take my cats for outdoor walks:	❏ YES	❏ NO
If YES, my cat walks on a harness:	❏ YES	❏ NO
My cat rides in a stroller:	❏ YES	❏ NO

Name of cat being rehomed:

Time of day my cat is the most active: *(Circle all)*

Morning   Daytime   Dusk   Nighttime

My cat's playtime with me is usually:

My cat's favorite toys are:

My cat's favorite game to play with a human is:

I take my cats for outdoor walks:	❑ YES	❑ NO
If YES, my cat walks on a harness:	❑ YES	❑ NO
My cat rides in a stroller:	❑ YES	❑ NO

Name of cat being rehomed:

Time of day my cat is the most active: *(Circle all)*

Morning   Daytime   Dusk   Nighttime

My cat's playtime with me is usually:

My cat's favorite toys are:

My cat's favorite game to play with a human is:

I take my cats for outdoor walks:	❏ YES	❏ NO
If YES, my cat walks on a harness:	❏ YES	❏ NO
My cat rides in a stroller:	❏ YES	❏ NO

🐾 Exercising your cat has several benefits: first and foremost, exercise, in addition to a moderate diet, will help keep your cat at a healthy weight. Pet obesity is an increasing problem in the United States. Secondly, exercise will minimize your cat's anxiety and boredom. Remember, there is a correlation between destructive behaviors and cats that do not get enough adequate, daily exercise.

🐾 If you only have only one cat, for exercise benefits and companionship, it should be a consideration to get a second cat; your local animal shelter or cat rescue can assist you in determining a favorable family addition. Similar age and energy level are the most important factors when seeking a compatible companion.

🐾 While Laser pointers are perceived as a fun toy that cat owners can use to initiate play, they do not fulfill a cat's complete prey sequence; the prey sequence consists of: 1) staring; 2) stalking and chasing 3) pouncing and grabbing and 4) kill bite. With laser pointers, they can't grab on to anything and there's nothing to bite, so completing the prey sequence is not possible and this can end up leaving a cat more frustrated.

🐾 A recommended toy for your cat is *Da Bird* (available on Amazon) which is an interactive, wand toy that comes with interchangeable lures; change your lures periodically to keep your cat from becoming bored.

🐾 Use caution when selecting cat toys with small pieces that may easily break off; these can cause choking and/or ingestion hazards. Toys with string should be put away when cats are alone, because choking and entanglement are potential hazards. Plastic bags commonly used in grocery stores are also a particular hazard due to choking and entanglement.

🐾 Cats are crepuscular animals, which means they are most active at dawn and dusk; to help ensure your cat isn't overly active during the night, it is best to play with them at dusk, and then follow with dinner.

🐾 Only about 80% of cats react to catnip, but a word of caution: it can cause rare aggression. Catnip alternatives worthy of consideration include Silvervine, Honeysuckle Spray and Valerian Root. Consult your veterinarian for more information.

🐾 While the physical benefits of exercise and playtime is well known for combating obesity in cats, Cats can absolutely benefit from mental engagement during their playtime, as well. The book, *Beyond Squeaky Toys*, by Cinthia Alia Mitchell and Nicole Nicassio-Hiskey, addresses the need for 'environmental enrichment' for cats (and dog s) to thwart boredom, and destructive/unwanted behavior.

Notes:

Name of cat being rehomed:		
My cat is only left alone for a maximum of _____ hours.		
My cat has access to the entire house while I'm away:	❑ YES	❑ NO
If NO, what areas are off limits?		
My cat needs TV or music left on:	❑ YES	❑ NO
My cat needs certain lighting:	❑ YES	❑ NO
If YES, please explain:		
My cat receives special treats or toys before I leave:	❑ YES	❑ NO
If YES, please explain:		
My cat has a pet sitter that comes as needed:	❑ YES	❑ NO
If YES, answer the following questions about your pet sitter: How often does the pet sitter come?		
How long is the pet sitter's normal visit?		
My pet sitter fulfills these duties during each visit:		
What is the agreed upon payment?		
Pet sitter's contact information:		

Name of cat being rehomed:

My cat is only left alone for a maximum of _____ hours.

My cat has access to the entire house while I'm away: ❏ YES ❏ NO

If NO, what areas are off limits?

My cat needs TV or music left on: ❏ YES ❏ NO

My cat needs certain lighting: ❏ YES ❏ NO

If YES, please explain:

My cat receives special treats or toys before I leave: ❏ YES ❏ NO

If YES, please explain:

My cat has a pet sitter that comes as needed: ❏ YES ❏ NO

If YES, answer the following questions about your pet sitter:
How often does the pet sitter come?

How long is the pet sitter's normal visit?

My pet sitter fulfills these duties during each visit:

What is the agreed upon payment?

Pet sitter's contact information:

Name of cat being rehomed:

My cat is only left alone for a maximum of _____ hours.

My cat has access to the entire house while I'm away:	❏ YES	❏ NO

If NO, what areas are off limits?

My cat needs TV or music left on:	❏ YES	❏ NO
My cat needs certain lighting:	❏ YES	❏ NO

If YES, please explain:

My cat receives special treats or toys before I leave:	❏ YES	❏ NO

If YES, please explain:

My cat has a pet sitter that comes as needed:	❏ YES	❏ NO

If YES, answer the following questions about your pet sitter:
How often does the pet sitter come?

How long is the pet sitter's normal visit?

My pet sitter fulfills these duties during each visit:

What is the agreed upon payment?

Pet sitter's contact information:

Name of cat being rehomed:	

My cat is only left alone for a maximum of _____ hours.

My cat has access to the entire house while I'm away:	❏ YES	❏ NO

If NO, what areas are off limits?

My cat needs TV or music left on:	❏ YES	❏ NO
My cat needs certain lighting:	❏ YES	❏ NO

If YES, please explain:

My cat receives special treats or toys before I leave:	❏ YES	❏ NO

If YES, please explain:

My cat has a pet sitter that comes as needed:	❏ YES	❏ NO

If YES, answer the following questions about your pet sitter:
How often does the pet sitter come?

How long is the pet sitter's normal visit?

My pet sitter fulfills these duties during each visit:

What is the agreed upon payment?

Pet sitter's contact information:

🐾 Separation anxiety can be a problem for some cats, and some cats become destructive out of boredom and frustration. Establishing a regular routine consisting of playtime and then feeding your cat prior to you leaving should help curb your cat's anxiety. For additional help with your cat's separation anxiety consult a cat behaviorist or your veterinarian.

🐾 Again, if you leave on a radio or TV for your cat while away, be conscious of your selection. Quiet, calm and soothing sounds will serve your cat best.

🐾 If your cat wears a collar in the house, consider removing it when you leave or use a Velcro cat collar that a cat could escape from. Collars can get caught up on or stuck in various places, causing entrapment or possible hanging, so please use careful deliberation.

🐾 **DO YOUR DUE DILIGENCE** in researching and interviewing prospective cat walkers and pet sitters. Regardless of the company who employs them or their professional affiliation, **ask to see referrals and reviews.** Never make assumptions about individuals you will be entrusting to care for your cat(s). A professional pet sitter should be able to provide proof of insurance, bonding and a background check. A great resource to look for reputable pet sitters in your area can be found through the **National Association of Professional Pet Sitters** at:
➡ **Petsitters.org**

Notes:

Name of cat being rehomed:		
My cat is professionally groomed:	❑ YES	❑ NO

Professional Grooming Information

Provide the name of your grooming salon and contact information for your groomer:

How often is your cat professionally groomed?

What does your groomer typically charge?

Additional services I request of my groomer:

NAIL TRIM	❑ YES	❑ NO
EAR CLEANING	❑ YES	❑ NO
ANAL GLANDS	❑ YES	❑ NO
TEETH BRUSHING	❑ YES	❑ NO

OTHER:

At Home Grooming Information

I wash my cat in the: (Circle one)

Tub   Shower   Utility sink   Other:

I brush my cat's hair this often?

I brush my cat's teeth this often?

I cut my cat's nails this often:
Circle one: FRONT   BACK

Location of grooming equipment:

Name of cat being rehomed:

My cat is professionally groomed: ❑ YES ❑ NO

Professional Grooming Information

Provide the name of your grooming salon and contact information for your groomer:

How often is your cat professionally groomed?

What does your groomer typically charge?

Additional services I request of my groomer:

NAIL TRIM ❑ YES ❑ NO

EAR CLEANING ❑ YES ❑ NO

ANAL GLANDS ❑ YES ❑ NO

TEETH BRUSHING ❑ YES ❑ NO

OTHER:

At Home Grooming Information

I wash my cat in the: (Circle one)

Tub   Shower   Utility sink   Other:

I brush my cat's hair this often?

I brush my cat's teeth this often?

I cut my cat's nails this often:
Circle one: FRONT   BACK

Location of grooming equipment:

Name of cat being rehomed:

My cat is professionally groomed: ❑ YES ❑ NO

Professional Grooming Information

Provide the name of your grooming salon and contact information for your groomer:

How often is your cat professionally groomed?

What does your groomer typically charge?

Additional services I request of my groomer:

NAIL TRIM ❑ YES ❑ NO

EAR CLEANING ❑ YES ❑ NO

ANAL GLANDS ❑ YES ❑ NO

TEETH BRUSHING ❑ YES ❑ NO

OTHER:

At Home Grooming Information

I wash my cat in the: (Circle one)

Tub Shower Utility sink Other:

I brush my cat's hair this often?

I brush my cat's teeth this often?

I cut my cat's nails this often:
Circle one: FRONT BACK

Location of grooming equipment:

Name of cat being rehomed:		
My cat is professionally groomed:	❑ YES	❑ NO

Professional Grooming Information

Provide the name of your grooming salon and contact information for your groomer:

How often is your cat professionally groomed?

What does your groomer typically charge?

Additional services I request of my groomer:

NAIL TRIM	❑ YES	❑ NO
EAR CLEANING	❑ YES	❑ NO
ANAL GLANDS	❑ YES	❑ NO
TEETH BRUSHING	❑ YES	❑ NO

OTHER:

At Home Grooming Information

I wash my cat in the: (Circle one)

Tub   Shower   Utility sink   Other:

I brush my cat's hair this often?

I brush my cat's teeth this often?

I cut my cat's nails this often:
Circle one: FRONT   BACK

Location of grooming equipment:

Helpful Tips!

🐾 Many cats dislike going to the groomer. It is advisable to acclimate your cat to grooming practices at a young age while using plenty of positive reinforcement. Fearfreehappyhomes.com is a great resource with suggestions to help alleviate your cat's fears under different circumstances.

🐾 If you must select a new groomer, pay attention to details: Is the facility clean? How does the staff act toward the animals? Are you allowed to stay and watch what they do? Consider getting recommendations from family and friends as well as online reviews.

🐾 Most cats do not like cage dryers; ask the groomer how they handle drying the cats: Do they use hand blow dryers? Is it a timed (heated or cool air) dryer kennel?

🐾 Some useful nail trimming tips include: wrapping your cat in a towel and only concentrating on one paw at a time, and if using human nail clippers, turning the clippers sideways as to not split the nail. *Kwik Stop* should be kept on hand in the event of bleeding, otherwise flour applied to the nail should stop the bleeding within a minute.

🐾 Cats can absolutely benefit from regular tooth brushing, however, you should consult your veterinarian first to make sure your cat is healthy enough to endure such cleaning; your veterinarian can also recommend the best tools and techniques to use. Also remember to only use toothpaste formulated for cats.

Notes:

Name of cat being rehomed:		
My cat is litter box trained:	❏ YES	❏ NO
If YES, there is still an occasional accident:	❏ YES	❏ NO
My cat is used to a litter box with a hood:	❏ YES	❏ NO
My cat is used to only an uncovered litter box tray:	❏ YES	❏ NO
My cat uses a different litter box arrangement. Explain:		
My cat uses this type and brand of litter:		
My cat MUST NOT use this type of litter:		
I clean my cat's litter box this often:		

Name of cat being rehomed:		
My cat is litter box trained:	❏ YES	❏ NO
If YES, there is still an occasional accident:	❏ YES	❏ NO
My cat is used to a litter box with a hood:	❏ YES	❏ NO
My cat is used to only an uncovered litter box tray:	❏ YES	❏ NO

My cat uses a different litter box arrangement. Explain:

My cat uses this type and brand of litter:

My cat MUST NOT use this type of litter:

I clean my cat's litter box this often:

77

Name of cat being rehomed:		
My cat is litter box trained:	❏ YES	❏ NO
If YES, there is still an occasional accident:	❏ YES	❏ NO
My cat is used to a litter box with a hood:	❏ YES	❏ NO
My cat is used to only an uncovered litter box tray:	❏ YES	❏ NO
My cat uses a different litter box arrangement. Explain:		
My cat uses this type and brand of litter:		
My cat MUST NOT use this type of litter:		
I clean my cat's litter box this often:		

Name of cat being rehomed:		
My cat is litter box trained:	❑ YES	❑ NO
If YES, there is still an occasional accident:	❑ YES	❑ NO
My cat is used to a litter box with a hood:	❑ YES	❑ NO
My cat is used to only an uncovered litter box tray:	❑ YES	❑ NO
My cat uses a different litter box arrangement. Explain:		
My cat uses this type and brand of litter:		
My cat MUST NOT use this type of litter:		
I clean my cat's litter box this often:		

🐾 Litter boxes should be cleaned every day, and houses having multiple cats should ideally have a litter box for each cat plus an extra one.

🐾 If you live in a dwelling with multiple floors, it is ideal to have a litter box on each floor.

🐾 If your cat has been used to non-scented litter, it is recommended to NOT change to a scented litter as the smell may be overwhelming to your cat, particularly in a litter box that has a hood on it. Cats may also have a sensitivity to air fresheners. Regular litter box cleaning combined with adding baking soda to the box should sufficiently keep odors to a minimum.

🐾 Declawed cats have been known to have problems with traditional rocky/crystallized litter; because of the sensitivity in their paw tips they may develop an aversion to litter box because of pain. Only use a fine, soft kitty litter with declawed cats.

🐾 Cats who suddenly start having accidents outside of the litter box may be suffering from a UTI or other physical Illness; after ruling out any possible environmental changes that may have contributed to this behavior, consult your veterinarian right away.

Notes:

Name of cat being rehomed:

My cat has a normal bedtime of:

My cat usually gets up at this time:

During the day, my cat likes to sleep (e.g., where, when, how):

At nighttime, my cat likes to sleep (e.g., where, when, how):

My cat's preferred spot to sleep in my bed is:

| My cat likes to be under covers or inside pillows: | ❏ YES | ❏ NO |
| My cat requires assistance or stairs/ ramp to get in and out of my bed: | ❏ YES | ❏ NO |

My cat's favorite hiding place is:

Additional information or idiosyncrasies of my pet's sleeping habits (snoring, etc.):

Name of cat being rehomed:
My cat has a normal bedtime of:
My cat usually gets up at this time:
During the day, my cat likes to sleep (e.g., where, when, how):
At nighttime, my cat likes to sleep (e.g., where, when, how):
My cat's preferred spot to sleep in my bed is:
My cat likes to be under covers or inside pillows: ❑ YES   ❑ NO
My cat requires assistance or stairs/ramp to get in and out of my bed: ❑ YES   ❑ NO
My cat's favorite hiding place is:
Additional information or idiosyncrasies of my pet's sleeping habits (snoring, etc.):

Name of cat being rehomed:

My cat has a normal bedtime of:

My cat usually gets up at this time:

During the day, my cat likes to sleep (e.g., where, when, how):

At nighttime, my cat likes to sleep (e.g., where, when, how):

My cat's preferred spot to sleep in my bed is:

My cat likes to be under covers or inside pillows: ❑ YES ❑ NO

My cat requires assistance or stairs/ramp to get in and out of my bed: ❑ YES ❑ NO

My cat's favorite hiding place is:

Additional information or idiosyncrasies of my pet's sleeping habits (snoring, etc.):

| Name of cat being rehomed: |
| My cat has a normal bedtime of: |
| My cat usually gets up at this time: |
| During the day, my cat likes to sleep (e.g., where, when, how): |
| At nighttime, my cat likes to sleep (e.g., where, when, how): |
| My cat's preferred spot to sleep in my bed is: |

| My cat likes to be under covers or inside pillows: | ❑ YES | ❑ NO |
| My cat requires assistance or stairs/ramp to get in and out of my bed: | ❑ YES | ❑ NO |

| My cat's favorite hiding place is: |

| Additional information or idiosyncrasies of my pet's sleeping habits (snoring, etc.): |

Helpful Tips!

- Please be mindful of keeping clothes dryer doors closed at all times and checking that they dryers are empty prior to loading clothes! Cats have been known to crawl into and sleep in dryers, unbeknownst to their owners, resulting in tragic consequences.

- Cats enjoy lounging and looking out windows so consider getting your cat a 'perch' which acts as a platform your cat can lie on, which attaches to a windowsill. Cats are also fond of free-standing 'cat trees' which come in a variety of sizes and designs and can also be moved near a window.

- Be mindful of closet doors if your cat likes to sleep in closets, tucked away. Cats can become accidentally trapped in closets by unsuspecting humans. Articulate this habit to your cat's new guardian so they don't panic if the cat isn't readily found.

Notes:

IN THE CAR ♥

Name of cat being rehomed:

My cat likes car rides: ❏ YES ❏ NO

My cat generally travels in the: *(Circle one)*
Front seat Back seat Rear of SUV

To keep my cat safe, my cat usually travels in a: *(Circle one)*
Hard carrier Soft carrier Other:

My cat gets carsick: ❏ YES ❏ NO

If YES, then: If cat is medicated before car rides, please name medication, dosage and how long before the car ride medication is administered.

The protocol for traveling with my cat is (e.g., travels in a hard carrier in the back seat):

Name of cat being rehomed:

My cat likes car rides: ❏ YES ❏ NO

My cat generally travels in the: *(Circle one)*
Front seat   Back seat   Rear of SUV

To keep my cat safe, my cat usually travels in a: *(Circle one)*
Hard carrier   Soft carrier   Other:

My cat gets carsick: ❏ YES ❏ NO

If YES, then: If cat is medicated before car rides, please name medication, dosage and how long before the car ride medication is administered.

The protocol for traveling with my cat is (e.g., travels in a hard carrier in the back seat):

Name of cat being rehomed:

My cat likes car rides: ❏ YES   ❏ NO

My cat generally travels in the: *(Circle one)*
Front seat   Back seat   Rear of SUV

To keep my cat safe, my cat usually travels in a: *(Circle one)*
Hard carrier   Soft carrier   Other:

My cat gets carsick: ❏ YES   ❏ NO

If YES, then: If cat is medicated before car rides, please name medication, dosage and how long before the car ride medication is administered.

The protocol for traveling with my cat is (e.g., travels in a hard carrier in the back seat):

Name of cat being rehomed:
My cat likes car rides: ❏ YES   ❏ NO
My cat generally travels in the: *(Circle one)*   Front seat   Back seat   Rear of SUV
To keep my cat safe, my cat usually travels in a: *(Circle one)*   Hard carrier   Soft carrier   Other:
My cat gets carsick: ❏ YES   ❏ NO
If YES, then: If cat is medicated before car rides, please name medication, dosage and how long before the car ride medication is administered.
The protocol for traveling with my cat is (e.g., travels in a hard carrier in the back seat):

Helpful Tips!

- Never leave your cat in a locked car with no air-conditioning in temperatures at 70 degrees F or above. Temperatures can rise as quickly as 20 degrees in 10 minutes. Cats do not sweat like humans do and can overheat quickly and quite possibly die of heat stroke. As of August 2015, Illinois amended the Humane Care of Animals Act, making it a Class A misdemeanor, which is punishable by a fine of up to $2,500 or up to one year in jail. Details of this law can be found here:

  ➡ ilga.gov/legislation/ilcs/ilcs3.asp?ActID=1717&ChapterID=41

- Even if you feel your cat is calm enough to travel in a car unsecured, please put your cat in a crate or carrier seat belted in securely. Companion animals risk the possibility of serious injury or death in the event of a car crash, and this threat is magnified by the airbag deployment in the vehicle.

- If your cat suffers from carsickness, speak to your veterinarian about possible solutions; they can make behavioral suggestions and/or pharmaceutical recommendations, as well.

Notes:

Name of cat being rehomed:			
My cat has been socialized with other cats:	❑ YES	❑ NO	❑ UNKNOWN
My cat is good with men:	❑ YES	❑ NO	❑ UNKNOWN
My cat is good with women:	❑ YES	❑ NO	❑ UNKNOWN
My cat is good with children:	❑ YES	❑ NO	❑ UNKNOWN
My cat is good with strangers coming to door:	❑ YES	❑ NO	❑ UNKNOWN
My cat will chase rabbits, squirrels, etc.:	❑ YES	❑ NO	❑ UNKNOWN
My cat will chase or harass smaller pets in the house:	❑ YES	❑ NO	❑ UNKNOWN
Explanation:			
My cat likes the mail delivery person:	❑ YES	❑ NO	❑ UNKNOWN
My cat does NOT get along with these additional pets or individuals:			
List your cat's love interests and/or playmates:			
List your cat's sworn enemies:			

Name of cat being rehomed:			
My cat has been socialized with other cats:	❑ YES	❑ NO	❑ UNKNOWN
My cat is good with men:	❑ YES	❑ NO	❑ UNKNOWN
My cat is good with women:	❑ YES	❑ NO	❑ UNKNOWN
My cat is good with children:	❑ YES	❑ NO	❑ UNKNOWN
My cat is good with strangers coming to door:	❑ YES	❑ NO	❑ UNKNOWN
My cat will chase rabbits, squirrels, etc.:	❑ YES	❑ NO	❑ UNKNOWN
My cat will chase or harass smaller pets in the house:	❑ YES	❑ NO	❑ UNKNOWN
Explanation:			
My cat likes the mail delivery person:	❑ YES	❑ NO	❑ UNKNOWN
My cat does NOT get along with these additional pets or individuals:			
List your cat's love interests and/or playmates:			
List your cat's sworn enemies:			

Name of cat being rehomed:			
My cat has been socialized with other cats:	❑ YES	❑ NO	❑ UNKNOWN
My cat is good with men:	❑ YES	❑ NO	❑ UNKNOWN
My cat is good with women:	❑ YES	❑ NO	❑ UNKNOWN
My cat is good with children:	❑ YES	❑ NO	❑ UNKNOWN
My cat is good with strangers coming to door:	❑ YES	❑ NO	❑ UNKNOWN
My cat will chase rabbits, squirrels, etc.:	❑ YES	❑ NO	❑ UNKNOWN
My cat will chase or harass smaller pets in the house:	❑ YES	❑ NO	❑ UNKNOWN

Explanation:

My cat likes the mail delivery person:	❑ YES	❑ NO	❑ UNKNOWN

My cat does NOT get along with these additional pets or individuals:

List your cat's love interests and/or playmates:

List your cat's sworn enemies:

Name of cat being rehomed:			
My cat has been socialized with other cats:	❏ YES	❏ NO	❏ UNKNOWN
My cat is good with men:	❏ YES	❏ NO	❏ UNKNOWN
My cat is good with women:	❏ YES	❏ NO	❏ UNKNOWN
My cat is good with children:	❏ YES	❏ NO	❏ UNKNOWN
My cat is good with strangers coming to door:	❏ YES	❏ NO	❏ UNKNOWN
My cat will chase rabbits, squirrels, etc.:	❏ YES	❏ NO	❏ UNKNOWN
My cat will chase or harass smaller pets in the house:	❏ YES	❏ NO	❏ UNKNOWN
Explanation:			
My cat likes the mail delivery person:	❏ YES	❏ NO	❏ UNKNOWN
My cat does NOT get along with these additional pets or individuals:			
List your cat's love interests and/or playmates:			
List your cat's sworn enemies:			

🐾 Positive experiences are very important when introducing cats for the first time. Dr. Marci Koski offers some great insight in her blog article on the subject.

👉 **www.felinebehaviorsolutions.com/cat-introductions-101-patience/**

🐾 Socializing your cat, particularly at a young age, is essential in helping your cat learn proper etiquette among his or her peers. Cats that do not get to socialize are more likely to grow up maladjusted.

Notes:

Name of cat being rehomed:

Please list any certifications, titles, and/or special designations your cat holds here:

Certifications:

Titles:

Special Designations:

Name of cat being rehomed:

Please list any certifications, titles, and/or special designations your cat holds here:

Certifications:

Titles:

Special Designations:

Notes:

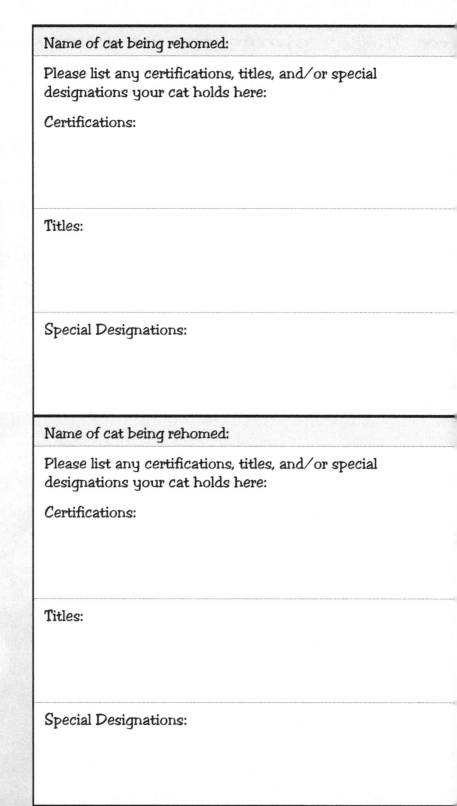

CERTIFICATIONS

Name of cat being rehomed:

Please list any certifications, titles, and/or special designations your cat holds here:

Certifications:

Titles:

Special Designations:

Name of cat being rehomed:

Please list any certifications, titles, and/or special designations your cat holds here:

Certifications:

Titles:

Special Designations:

Notes:

Animal Sanctuaries that allow your cat to live at their facility for the remainder of their life; facilities marked with an asterisk (*) will offer you a Rehoming option for your cat as well; please contact each organization for specific information.

Best Friends Animal Society KANUB, UT
(435) 644-2001
bestfriends.org

Cat House on The Kings* PARLIER, CA
Cathouseonthekings.com

Cat Tail Acres* SHELBY TOWNSHIP, MI
Cattailacres.com

Home for Life STILLWATER, MN
(800) 252-5918
homeforlife.org

House with a Heart Senior Pet Sanctuary GAITHERSBURG, MD
(240) 631-1743
housewithaheart.com

PLEASE NOTE: The author of this book does not have personal or professional experience with these organizations and cannot guarantee the quality of care that they provide or their ability to accommodate your cat(s). Therefore, you are encouraged to conduct independent research of these organizations to determine whether any of them fit your wishes; the author also cannot guarantee that they are still in operation.

Rehoming organizations that allow your cat to live at their facility OR will adopt them out to an individual home; please contact each organization for specific information:

Hearts United for Animals AUBURN, NE
(402) 274-3679
hua.org

The Milo Foundation WILLITS, CA
(707) 459-4900
milofoundation.org

Oasis Animal Sanctuary FRANKLINVILLE, NJ
(856) 262-1222
oasisanimalsanctuary.org

PAWS Guardian Angel Program CHICAGO, IL
(773) 697-5207
Pawschicago.com

Safe Place for Pets COLORADO SPRINGS, CO
(719) 359-0201
safeplacepets.org

Specialty Purebred Cat Rescue SOMERS, WI
Specialtypurebredcatrescue.org

The Cat-Cade CHICAGO, IL
The catcade.org

The Odd Cat Sanctuary SALEM, MA
Theoddcatsanctuary.com

PLEASE NOTE: The author of this book does not have personal or professional experience with these organizations and cannot guarantee the quality of care that they provide or their ability to accommodate your cat(s). Therefore, you are encouraged to conduct independent research of these organizations to determine whether any of them fit your wishes; the author also cannot guarantee that they are still in operation.

ANIMAL SERVICES

The Cat Fanciers' Association (CFA.) • CFA.org

Chris Unangst, 2008 TICA International Judge of the Year   TOLEDO, OH

Crossroads Animal Hospital   CROWN POINT, IN
CrossroadsAnimalHospital.org

Datamars, Microchip Scanner Manufacturer • Datamars.com

Dreamquete Exotic Shorthairs and Persians   HOBART, IN
Cheryl Hague, TICA Breeder/Exhibitor of International and Regional
winning cats. • Dreamquete@yahoo.com • Dreamquete.com

Famous Fido Rescue Wellness & Learning Center   CHICAGO, IL
Gloria Lissner, Founder • Famousfidorescue.com

Feline Behavior Solutions   VANCOUVER, WA
Dr. Marci L. Koski, Certified Feline Behavior & Training Consultant
(503) 927-1107 • marci@felinebehaviorsolutions.com •
FelineBehaviorSolutions.com

Good Karma Pet Services, LLC   CHICAGO, IL
Facebook.com/goodkarmapetsitting

Help Finding Lost Cats in Illinois • Lostcatsillinois.org
Facebook.com/lostcatsillinois

Kitty City Salon   PALATINE, IL
Cathy Hartly, C.M.G. Certified Master Groomer, C.F.M. Certified
Feline Master Groomer • (847) 533-2807 • kittycitysalon.com

Pawsitively Heaven   CHICAGO RIDGE, IL
Judith Schnur, Proprietress of cat and cat boarding facility,
Pawsitivelyheavenpetresort.com

Pet Poison Helpline • 800-213-6680
($59 per incident with follow-up call)

The International Cat Association (TICA.) • TICA.org

What About The Dog? • whataboutthedogbook.com

PLEASE NOTE: The author of this book does not have personal or professional
experience with these organizations and cannot guarantee the quality of care
that they provide or their ability to accommodate your cat(s). Therefore, you are
encouraged to conduct independent research of these organizations to determine
whether any of them fit your wishes; the author also cannot guarantee that they
are still in operation.

106

OTHER SERVICES

MOMENTUM Creative Integration, Stacey Edge
Creative Design Firm ▪ momentum-ci.com

NextHome Select Realty, Christine Ciana Calabrese
Illinois Licensed Realtor ▪ m.facebook.com/ChristineCianaCalabreseRealtor
HomebuyingISpossible.com

OK Silly Ink, Sharon Sprague
Writer and Designer ▪ oksilly.com

Women Conquer Business, Jen McFarland
Business Coach for Women ▪ Jenmcfarland.com

Zarzecki Law, Charles Zarzecki
Estate Planning Attorney/Pet Trusts ▪ Zarzeckilawgroup.com

Others:

Christine Ciana Calabrese is a longtime animal lover, advocate and rescuer. She currently owns and operates the business, Good Karma Pet Sitting and authored the book *What About the Dog?*. Christine is the proud pet parent of Karma, a Cairn Terrier, Tapioca, a Chihuahua-mix, Olive, a Shih-Tzu, Pippy, a little demon disguised as a Chihuahua, and two parakeets named Napoleon and Josephine (commonly referred to as "Budgies").

HOW TO PURCHASE ADDITIONAL COPIES

 If you have found this book helpful and would like to purchase additional copies for the cat lovers in your life, please visit **Amazon.com**.

For wholesale inquiries, please e-mail Whataboutthecatbook@gmail.com.

 Whataboutthecatbook

 Facebook.com/Whataboutthecatbook

 whataboutthecatbook.com

Notes:

Made in the USA
Monee, IL
21 August 2020